W.i.t.c.h.
Will   Irma   Taranee   Cornelia   Hay Lin

Annual 2007

Editor: Anne Ewart   Designer: Laura Bird

EGMONT
We bring stories to life

First published in Great Britain in 2006 by Egmont UK Limited, 239 Kensington High Street, London W8 6SA
© Disney

ISBN 978 1 4052 2603 5
ISBN 1 4052 2603 X
1 3 5 7 9 10 8 6 4 2
Printed in Italy

Welcome ...

to our super-cool W.I.T.C.H. Annual 2007. It's jam-packed with puzzles, comics and fab advice – enough to cast a spell on you all year round. You can even add up your scores on the puzzle pages to find your own W.I.T.C.H. level. Have fun! Love,

The W.I.T.C.H. girls are best friends who share an amazing secret – they each have super-special magical powers!

Taranee

Cornelia

Hay Lin

Irma

Will

Here's what's inside!

The world of W.I.T.C.H.

The Heart of Candracar

When Will Vandom moves to Heatherfield and a new school, Sheffield Institute, she soon makes friends with Irma Lair, Taranee Cook, Cornelia Hale and Hay Lin.

Five ordinary girls in an ordinary school, they quickly become the closest friends you'll ever meet - but their friendship is not accidental. When they're together, strange things start happening to them. They begin to wonder, did they meet by chance or is there a stronger force at work?

Then Will is given a rare medallion, the Heart of Candracar, and is revealed to be its special Guardian. The other girls discover their own extraordinary powers too, as the Guardians of the elements earth, air, water and fire.

Together they are W.I.T.C.H. and combine to form a friendship more powerful than they could ever have imagined!

Will   **I**rma   **T**aranee   **C**ornelia   **H**ay Lin

W.I.T.C.H. friendship is ...

Bursting out laughing together – especially when it's uncalled for!

Buying the same bracelets but with different colours!

8

Will Vandom

Will is the leader of the group. She is the Guardian of the Heart of Candracar and has power over absolute energy.

ENERGY

Irma Lair

Irma has been given power over the element water. She can control the seas and cause tidal waves.

WATER

Taranee Cook

Taranee has been given power over the element fire and is able to create swirling flames with her hands.

FIRE

Cornelia Hale

With the power over the element earth, Cornelia can create little earthquakes and make plants grow on command.

EARTH

Hay Lin

Hay Lin has power over the element air. She can unleash a tornado as well as being able to fly.

AIR

Read on to join in their exciting adventures, share in their magical secret and discover the power of friendship!

Cheering her on in whatever she does!

Learning the words to the same song by heart!

9

HI, I'M WILL

- I'm a Capricorn
- My birthday is January 19th
- I sometimes feel shy but I'm also stubborn and sensitive
- I have a crush on Matt (the school heart throb)!
- My favourite colour is fuschia
- I collect all sorts of cute frog-shaped things
- I have a pet dormouse

AS A W.I.T.C.H.

- I'm the leader of the group
- My power is energy and I can use my power to strengthen the other Witches' powers
- I can see my enemies' auras

MY POWER IS ENERGY

AMULETS

Will's amulet, or lucky charm, is the Heart of Candracar. It may look like any old pendant, but Will's amulet reminds her that the most magical part of herself is inside, ready to be called on at any time.

Do you have a lucky charm? It can be anything, but it must follow this simple rule – your lucky charm must be found or given to you as a gift. Why? Easy! Because it must find you, not the other way round! Don't forget that the secret of an amulet's strength is ...

Imagination!

Good LUCK? It's believing you are lucky!

Legend has it that keeping a coin minted in the year of your birth will bring you lots of money. (Attention all mums and dads!)

Catch a falling leaf and keep it for good luck. (Don't do it at school though because if a cute boy's around you're bound to trip over!)

Wear an item of clothing inside out for a whole day and it'll bring you good luck! (You might even start a new trend – you never know!)

A SMILE will always bring you GOOD LUCK

Lucky charm

THE HEATHERFIELD MALL. AMONG THE BUSTLING CROWDS OF PEOPLE ...

... IS SOMEONE WHO'S JUST HAD A DISAPPOINTMENT.

THAT'S ENOUGH, SARAH! WE'VE TRIED WITH ONE COIN AND I'M NOT GIVING YOU ANOTHER ONE.

BUT I WANNA WIN THE RING!

IT'S TIME FOR US TO GO! JACK'S WAITING FOR US.

JAAACK! WHERE ARE YOU?

BOO HOO ...

STAND BACK, FOLKS! TODAY THE WITCHES ARE READY FOR ONE WICKED SHOPPING SPREE!

ER, ACTUALLY ...

THIS IS ALL I'VE GOT!

13

THE END

The alarm clock!

20 pts

Which clock below shows the correct time if one clock is 10 minutes fast, another is 15 minutes slow, a third has stopped and the last is 20 minutes fast?

A

B

C

D

E

5 pts

Who's meeting who?

Can you read this secret note? All you do is replace each letter following the code below –

A B C D E F G H I J K L M N O P Q R S T U V W X Y Z
Z A B C D E F G H I J K L M N O P Q R S T U Z W X Y

IJ XJMM!

XBOU UP HP PO

B CJLF SJEF BGUFS

TDIPPM?

17

Power match

10 pts

Can you match together the halves to make the five W.I.T.C.H. symbols?

Quick search

5 pts

Which two close-ups below don't appear in Hay Lin's room?

ecrets to?

7

WHAT DO YOU DO AFTER
ARGUING WITH YOUR PARENTS?
A Phone your best mate
   (go to profile T)
B Lock yourself in your room
   (go to profile H)

W
Profile W - YOUR FRIENDS
You firmly believe in friendship. Whenever something happens (good or bad), you can't wait to share it with your mates.
You can't stand – to see your friends arguing!
You would like – to go on holiday with your friends!

I
Profile I - A SHARED DIARY
You're someone who loves to joke around and have fun. If needed, though, you can be serious and give good advice.
You can't stand – to find out that your secrets have been given away!
You would like – your dreams to come true!

T
Profile T - YOUR OWN DIARY
You are shy but firm. You don't like to be the centre of attention, but you soon speak up when you don't agree with something.
You can't stand – to be left out!
You would like – to express yourself more easily!

C
Profile C - YOUR BEST FRIEND
You think very hard before telling your secrets to anyone, even your best friend. You have to be sure that they can be trusted.
You can't stand – not to be taken seriously!
You would like – to be thought of as the ideal friend by everyone!

H
Profile H - YOUR EMAIL
You like being with your friends but you also like being on your own. You listen well and are always ready to offer your help.
You can't stand – to be criticised!
You would like – to show how fun you can be!

HI, I'M IRMA

- I'm a Pisces
- My birthday is March 13th
- I'm the most feminine of the group – I love to dance, sing and imitate famous actresses and singers
- I really hate all sports
- I'm terrified of spiders and the dark
- My favourite subject at school is art
- My favourite colour is turquoise
- I tell all my secrets to my pet turtle, Leafy

AS A W.I.T.C.H.

- My power is water and I can control all liquids
- I'm also telepathic!

MY POWER IS WATER

23

Objective: survival

IRMA!

IRMA! IT'S TIME TO GET UP!

HEY! WHAT? ALREADY?

DON'T TAKE AGES, AS USUAL. REMEMBER YOU HAVE A BROTHER.

ME FIRST!

CHRISTOPHER! I'LL BE LATE FOR SCHOOL!

THE END

25

The power of WATER

... it's truly magical!

Irma knows how powerful water can be. Its magical qualities mean that it can appear in many different forms – a sparkling liquid, solid ice and even a steaming vapour. Whatever its form, the power of water can make the most amazing things happen. Water is ...

Water is CLEANSING, PURE, FUN!

... essential for the life of plants and animals.

... fantastic fun! Like the first swim of the summer in the sea, or diving and playing with friends.

... luxurious, as a hot and steamy sauna.

... as refreshing as a mountain stream.

Water is a great cleanser – and not just for the body. Bad thoughts can also be washed away with a shower or a warm bath.

Shell search

Which two groups of shells below look exactly the same?

Hey, Irma!
Love your shells!

Taranee

Word wonder

Give yourself five minutes and see if you can make 10 words, of three letters or more, from the name of the W.I.T.C.H. girls' school?

Sheffield Institute

Got more than ten? You're a genius!

Discover your style

Which season's colours suit YOU best?
Try this quiz to find out!

1 YOUR EYES ARE ...
B Blue
A Green
C Brown
D Grey

2 YOUR HAIR IS ...
C Ginger
B Blonde
A Brown
D Black

3 WEARING A YELLOW HAT MAKES YOU LOOK ...
D Fantastic!
B Very ill
A Overwhelmed
C Seriously uncool

4 STANDING IN A PEACH-COLOURED ROOM MAKES YOU ...
C Want to run out
A The centre of attention
B Blend in with the walls
D Feel slightly sick

5 WHEN YOU'RE OUT IN THE GREEN COUNTRYSIDE ...
C People always notice your hair and eyes
B People mistake you for a tree!
D You're full of energy
A You like to decorate your hair with leaves

6 WEARING A PALE BLUE JUMPER MAKES YOU LOOK ...
A OK
D Washed out
B Elegant
C Really boring

7 WHEN IT COMES TO JEWELLERY, YOU LOOK BEST IN ...
A & C Gold
B & D Silver

Mostly As: You are spring

You look great in warm colours like peach, blue-green and golden brown. You should avoid wearing colours like mustard and orange.
Your spring style: relaxed and sporty in jeans and a T-shirt.
Good jewellery for you: coloured stones, especially turquoise.

A

Mostly Bs: You are summer

You look great in colours like pale pink, lavender, navy blue and white. You should avoid wearing colours like brown and light grey.
Your summer style: romantic with lots of lace and floaty fabrics.
Good jewellery for you: anything with pearls or white stones.

B

Mostly Cs: You are autumn

You look great in warm colours like golden-brown, camel, olive green and gold. You should avoid colours like grey, yellow and red.
Your autumn style: layer-up with different shades of the same colour.
Good jewellery for you: anything gold or bronze.

C

Mostly Ds: You are winter

You look good in cold, clear colours like black and white, and red, yellow and green. You should avoid colours like grey and pale blue.
Your winter style: simple styles with lots of accessories.
Good jewellery for you: silver with black stones.

D

Smile!

Which photo can be taken away to leave two of Will, two of Taranee, two of Cornelia, two of Irma and two of Hay Lin?

5 pts

Photo A

Irma's wearing a T-shirt with Karmilla on! Ha! Ha!

Photo B

Photo C

Photo D

Photo E

5 pts

Letter jumble

Cross out the letters of the W.I.T.C.H. girls' names from the letters on the right. Now, can you rearrange the leftovers to spell something Irma is fond of?

```
T A I E R C W A
R L E L N R E A E
H A L I A M A Y T
L I N O R I N W
```

31

Who you are: You're pure energy! You love sports and are always ready for a challenge.
Your magic power: Your enthusiasm and generosity will make this year a real giggle!
School: You're a fast learner but don't be afraid though to explore a subject in more depth.
Relationships: Be careful not to lose your temper – not everyone is as fast as you.
Look: Your usual style is comfortable and relaxed. Why not give the elegant look a try in 2007?

Who you are: You have the forces of nature behind you – it's time to make your dreams come true!
Your magic power: Your enchanting voice will cast a magic spell on someone special.
School: Working extra-hard in your language classes will soon prove useful!
Relationships: A misunderstanding will put a friendship in danger. Be loyal and your friendship will grow stronger.
Look: Don't be afraid to experiment – if it feels right, you'll look great!

Who you are: Your sensitivity to other people's needs is almost ... magical!
Your magic power: Your kindness has the power to open the door to an unexpected friendship.
School: A new hobby after school will bring exciting friends your way.
Relationships: Listening to your best friend's advice will really pay off.
Look: Try swapping clothes with a friend – it'll keep your wardrobe fresh!

your stars?

...ave in store for you in 2007!

Who you are: You're a true dreamer with your own secret inner world.

Your magic power: Your creativity and mischief will bring happiness to all your friends.

School: Your vivid imagination will make lessons much more fun but be careful not to get distracted.

Relationships: Remember that a problem shared is a problem halved.

Look: Be prepared for everyone to copy your funky style – how cool!

Who you are: This year, the world is your stage ... and the show won't begin without you!

Your magic power: Your sunshine glow will shine on all those around you.

School: Use your new confidence to always put on your best performance.

Relationships: Remember that other people like compliments just as much as you do!

Look: This year, spending less on fashion will help you create an individual style.

Who you are: You always plan ahead to make sure you don't miss any fun opportunities!

Your magic power: You're a good listener who can make magical decisions.

School: A boring school trip will turn into a great adventure!

Relationships: A rumour will cause confusion with your friends. Don't worry though, it will end in laughter – phew!

Look: Save up your pocket money to get what you want – it will definitely be worth the wait!

Libra 24th Sept – 23rd Oct

Who you are: You're great at making everyone around you feel comfortable in any situation.

Your magic power: Your well-chosen words will set others dreaming this year – you're a born W.I.T.C.H.

School: Prepare well for your lessons and you will feel much happier.

Friends: Listening to a friend's problem will help her out of a tricky situation.

Look: Feel like a change? A new haircut will give you a real boost.

Scorpio 24th Oct – 22nd Nov

Who you are: You're independent and are always looking ahead to see what's coming next.

Your magic power: You are the 'witchiest' W.I.T.C.H. there is – pure mystery!

School: This year your problem-solving skills will push you ahead in maths.

Friends: Sharing secrets with a mate will make your friendship even stronger.

Look: Throw out the black and layer on the bright colours!

Sagittarius 23rd Nov – 22nd Dec

Who you are: You're a true free spirit with an amazing sense of humour.

Your magic power: When your friends are down, you have the power to cheer them up.

School: Geography will be your subject this year but watch out for a tricky English test.

Relationships: An old friend is going to make a surprise appearance somewhere you least expect it!

Look: For that touch of glamour, throw on an extra piece of sparkling jewellery!

Who you are: Your strong character helps you to keep your dreams alive.

Your magic power: You know how to make people feel really good about themselves.

School: Your hard work will really pay off this year. Keep going – it will be worth it in the end.

Relationships: You're feeling a strong bond with a new friend. That's cool but don't forget your old friends!

Look: Keep to your natural style of elegant simplicity – it's greatly admired!

Who you are: You're as free as a brightly coloured butterfly, fluttering from flower to flower.

Your magic power: Your radical ideas will make people look at you in a different way.

School: Let your creative juices flow – especially when using a computer.

Relationships: Someone is missing you. Pick up the phone and give them a call – they'll be really pleased.

Look: Go with your instincts but be prepared to stand out in a crowd!

Who you are: You're an artistic dreamer who lives with your head in the clouds.

Your magic power: You know how to get in touch with other worlds. This power makes you unique.

School: Don't let homework get you down. Take it one subject at a time and you'll soon get through it.

Relationships: Helping a friend in need will make you both feel great.

Look: Your classic sense of style works well when you mix it with the latest accessories!

I have the power of FIRE. I can create whirls of fire, aggressive blazes and even fiery spheres that light up the darkness.

Classical music is my favourite

BUGS
I love to take pictures of them but I sure am terrified of them!

Nigel

COOK FAMILY
Lionel
Theresa Robson
Peter Lancelot
and ME!

Aries

I love basketball!

to love

COOK

Witch

HI, I'M TARANEE

- 🔘 I'm an Aries

- 🔘 My birthday is March 23rd

- 🔘 I'm shy, easygoing and clever – but I don't like studying too hard

- 🔘 I love maths, classical music and photography

- 🔘 I'm scared of all flying insects, no matter how small

- 🔘 I can be impulsive

- 🔘 I'm always losing my glasses

- 🔘 My favourite colour is red

AS A W.I.T.C.H.

- 🔘 I have the power of fire

- 🔘 I become so daring I even surprise myself

- 🔘 I can also reveal people's true personalities

MY POWER IS FIRE

THE END

BE CONFIDENT

Strange but true – almost everyone feels shy at some point. Time plays a very important part in making us feel more secure but remembering the simple points below will help you feel more positive and confident, straight away!

The magic of wishing is very powerful!

Don't give up before you begin

If you want something – ask for it. Don't imagine that the answer will be "no" before you've even asked! Remember, you can do anything you set your mind to – you just have to believe!

Put yourself in the other person's place

Everyone feels insecure when they don't know what to say or how to do something. Thinking that everyone is a little bit frightened will help you feel more at ease and less alone.

Stay positive

Imagine what you wish to happen and think about that. Having a positive attitude will help you stay confident. If something cringey happens, try to see the funny side and have a giggle with your friends.

Stand up and battle for WHAT YOU BELIEVE IN

20 pts

Magical wordsearch

Test your powers by finding all 10 words in the grid below.

- ENERGY
- SECRETS
- POWER
- FIRE
- AIR
- FRIENDSHIP
- EARTH
- WATER
- LUCKY CHARM
- MAGIC

```
M A G F R I E F W O S W A T
G T I G C G R I A G T O I G
D R F P O W D F T S E T D R
E M P I H S D N E I R F C E
N S A S K C U L R S C L P W
E H E G H T R A E A E O I O
R I U D I F I E N E S D H P
G P M L U C K Y C H A R M D
Y B L A I W A T B R M R T H
```

The mysterious picture

Taranee has mixed up photos of her friends to make a cool picture. Can you work out which picture part comes from which friend?

Tara –
your pics are
so ... W.I.T.C.H.!

5 pts

41

Truly magical

It's raining outside and you don't know what to do with your friends?
The W.I.T.C.H. girls are here to teach you some magic tricks for an enchanting afternoon!

The magic cards

You will need:
A pack of cards and some friends to see your 'powers'!

This trick is simple but very effective. Here's how to do it:
Split the pack of cards into three or four piles and place them on the table.

Ask a friend to choose one of the piles. Then, casually, start counting the number of cards in the pile.

Pretend to be concentrating and recite the following magic words: Fire ... Little fire ... Come close to me ... Help my art ... Increase the number of my cards ...

Give the pile back to your friend, asking her to count the cards again. WOW! Hey, Presto! The number of cards has increased and, of course, it's all down to your powers!

Solution:
When you count the cards for the first time, take one card from the bottom of the pile every now and then (making sure nobody notices) and count it with the one that is visible to the audience. This way, at the end of the counting, you will have more cards in the bunch than those the audience has heard you count out loud, and that they therefore believe to have seen in your hands!

W.I.T.C.H. tricks

Long-distance reading

You will need:
A dictionary, two toothpicks and an audience.

Here's how to impress your friends:
Hand a toothpick to a person in the audience.

Leave the room and after a while come back with a dictionary in your hand.

Casually walk towards the friend who has the toothpick and ask her to place it between any two pages of the dictionary.

Walk towards another person in the audience and give her the dictionary.

Now fake an intense concentration, wave your hands in the air, whisper something incomprehensible and ... you will be able to tell her the first words on each of the two pages the toothpicks were placed between!

Solution:
Of course you don't need magic powers to do this number. All you need is a little craftiness. Before you start, insert another toothpick inside the dictionary, making sure you don't forget the first word in each of the two pages. Casually take off the toothpick placed inside the dictionary by your unsuspecting friend to obtain the desired result.

YOGA: Control

YOGA increases your energy flow, improves your poise, strengthens your body and relaxes your mind.

Totally cool! READY?

Let's begin ...

Look at the pictures and try these basic yoga poses. You'll see, they're less complicated than they seem, except for their names (to be pronounced in public only after a lot of practice!)

1

Sukhasana
or "the easy pose"
by Hay Lin

Sit up straight with your legs crossed and your head up. Place your hands on your knees, palms upwards. Breathe deeply, closing your eyes. Relax.

This pose lengthens the spine and is good for inner calm. It's best after a stressful lesson in maths or history!

your energy

③

Shavasana
or "the relaxation pose"
by Taranee Cook

Lying on your back, let your arms and legs drop open, palms up. Relax. Breathe deeply and imagine you are at the seashore, listening to the lapping of the waves and the sound of the wind.

This pose is totally relaxing. Your breathing becomes calm and regular. 10 minutes of this exercise are worth 8 hours' sleep (tell your mum this when you want to stay up to watch your favourite TV programme!)

Bhujangasana
or "the cobra pose"
by Irma Lair

Lie flat on the floor. Put your hands under your shoulders. Lift your chest off the floor slowly, using your back muscles (not your arms). Hold the pose as long as you can, breathing easily. Then, slowly let yourself back down to the floor.

This pose re-awakens the energy lying within us. It's especially good on a Monday morning, when your body just won't wake up!

Ardha-Matsyendrasana
or "the lord of the fishes pose"
by Cornelia Hale

Sit on the floor with your legs straight out in front of you. Slide your right foot under your left thigh. Place your left foot over your right knee. Turn your torso to the left, place your right elbow on your left knee and press your left hand against the floor. Hold this pose as long as you can, then relax.

This pose stretches your shoulders and improves your posture. It's great for aspiring models and anyone who isn't afraid of getting tangled up!

④

②

TAURUS

THE POWER OF EARTH
The power to open passageways in
the ground, create microseisms, any.
The power to open, at will and change, any
walls or the ground, at will and change, any
make flower's bloom. Also the power to
kind of vegetation, with my mind.
move objects with my mind.

HALES
Harold, Elizabeth Langdon,
Cornelia, and Lillian.

NAPOLEON
Uriji gave him to me after
Caleb turned into a flower.

Cornelia Hale

CALEB
First I saw him in
my dreams, then
I met him in Meridian.

Witch
Will Irma Taranee Cornelia Hay Lin

HI, I'M CORNELIA

- My star sign is Taurus
- My birthday is May 10th
- I'm pretty confident and love to be up to date with the latest fashion
- I'm quiet, but when I say something I generally hit the nail on the head
- I love ice skating
- I have a fear of water and enclosed spaces
- I own a cat called Napoleon
- My favourite colour is green

AS A W.I.T.C.H.

- I control the power of earth
- I can sense the planet's lines of force
- I can move objects just by thinking

MY POWER IS EARTH

When things go wrong ...
DON'T PANIC!

The unexpected is always waiting to jump out at you – just when you expect it least. Whatever shocks come your way, try to remember these three W.I.T.C.H. tips –

Don't fear change

Change happens because nothing can stay the same forever. Feeling sad because of a change is normal because it's hard to leave what you know behind. Try to remember, though, that change often brings excitement instead of sadness – so enjoy the change and who knows what may happen!

Develop know-how

Developing know-how will help you to pull yourself out of all kinds of tricky situations much more easily. The basic rule is to do the right thing, at the right time, thinking of everyone else's feelings around you.

Give yourself another chance

You did all you could but it still didn't happen in the way you'd hoped. First of all, try not to let it get you down. Think of what you've learned from the experience and then move on. There will be plenty of other occasions, just around the corner, for you to prove how great you are!

Tell it how it is

MONDAY MORNING, IN CHARGE OF THE SCHOOL EDITORIAL OFFICE ...

I'VE FINISHED THE PIECE ON HEATHERFIELD, WHAT DO YOU THINK?

LET'S SEE ...

HEATHERFIELD, THE MOST BEAUTIFUL CITY IN THE WORLD! HOW ELSE COULD WE DESCRIBE THIS MAGNIFICENT PLACE?

... WET BY THE CLEANEST SEA ON THE COAST AND PROTECTED BY SWEET, GREEN HILLS, THE MOST FERTILE IN THE AREA ...

THE MOST BEAUTIFUL CITY IN THE WORLD ... CLEANEST SEA ... DON'T YOU THINK YOU'VE EXAGGERATED?

MMM ... NOW THAT I THINK OF IT ...

HEATHERFIELD! WHERE THE MOST EXAGGERATED PEOPLE IN THE CONTINENT LIVE!

THE END

Magic numbers

The numbers 1 to 16 can be fitted into this grid so that each horizontal and vertical line adds up to 34. Can you work out where missing numbers 1 to 5 fit?

15 pts

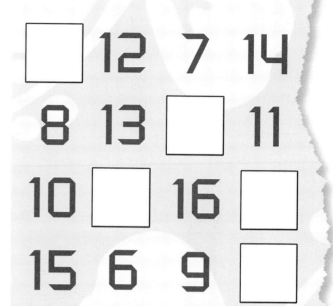

10 pts

Colour trail

Can you figure out which blue square leads to the red square?

50

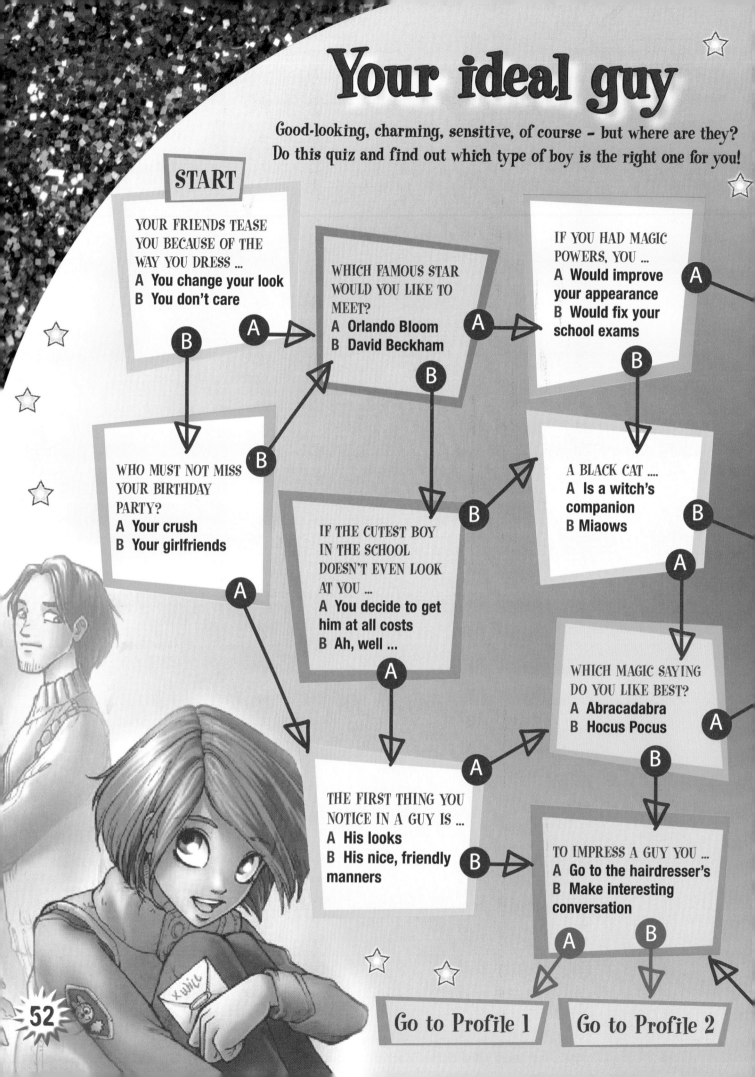

Your ideal guy

Good-looking, charming, sensitive, of course – but where are they?
Do this quiz and find out which type of boy is the right one for you!

START

YOUR FRIENDS TEASE YOU BECAUSE OF THE WAY YOU DRESS ...
A You change your look
B You don't care

WHICH FAMOUS STAR WOULD YOU LIKE TO MEET?
A Orlando Bloom
B David Beckham

IF YOU HAD MAGIC POWERS, YOU ...
A Would improve your appearance
B Would fix your school exams

WHO MUST NOT MISS YOUR BIRTHDAY PARTY?
A Your crush
B Your girlfriends

IF THE CUTEST BOY IN THE SCHOOL DOESN'T EVEN LOOK AT YOU ...
A You decide to get him at all costs
B Ah, well ...

A BLACK CAT ....
A Is a witch's companion
B Miaows

WHICH MAGIC SAYING DO YOU LIKE BEST?
A Abracadabra
B Hocus Pocus

THE FIRST THING YOU NOTICE IN A GUY IS ...
A His looks
B His nice, friendly manners

TO IMPRESS A GUY YOU ...
A Go to the hairdresser's
B Make interesting conversation

52

Go to Profile 1   Go to Profile 2

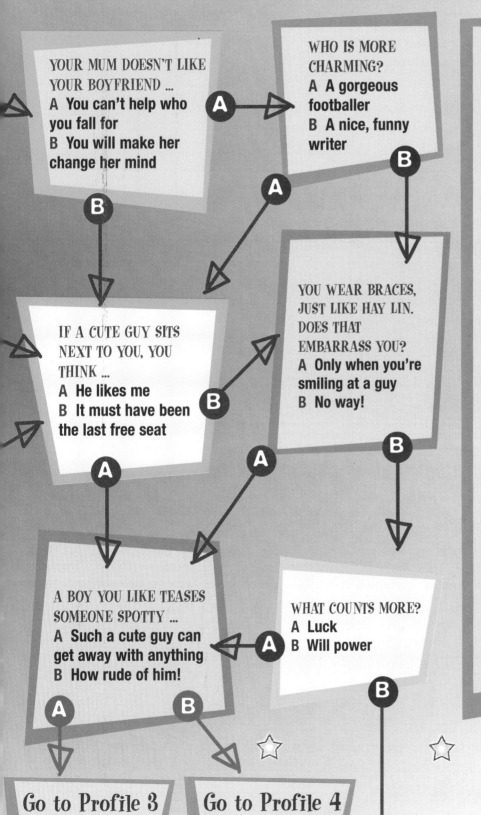

YOUR MUM DOESN'T LIKE YOUR BOYFRIEND ...
A You can't help who you fall for
B You will make her change her mind

WHO IS MORE CHARMING?
A A gorgeous footballer
B A nice, funny writer

IF A CUTE GUY SITS NEXT TO YOU, YOU THINK ...
A He likes me
B It must have been the last free seat

YOU WEAR BRACES, JUST LIKE HAY LIN. DOES THAT EMBARRASS YOU?
A Only when you're smiling at a guy
B No way!

A BOY YOU LIKE TEASES SOMEONE SPOTTY ...
A Such a cute guy can get away with anything
B How rude of him!

WHAT COUNTS MORE?
A Luck
B Will power

Profile 1 – You are dynamic and a fighter!
You like gorgeous, super-fit guys – and they need to be fit to keep up with you!
W.I.T.C.H. advice: Make sure you don't lose touch with what's really important.

Profile 2 – You are sweet and very affectionate
Your ideal boyfriend is kind and able to make you feel like the centre of the universe.
W.I.T.C.H. advice: Don't expect too much – heroes and knights only exist in books!

Profile 3 – You like to look after yourself
Your ideal boyfriend is handsome, cool and perfect in very way.
W.I.T.C.H. advice: Perfection doesn't last. Relax and try to look beyond appearances.

Profile 4 – You value respect and simplicity
Your ideal boyfriend is somebody who can listen and earn your trust.
W.I.T.C.H. advice: Remember to have fun. Your smile will make him happy, too.

Go to Profile 3

Go to Profile 4

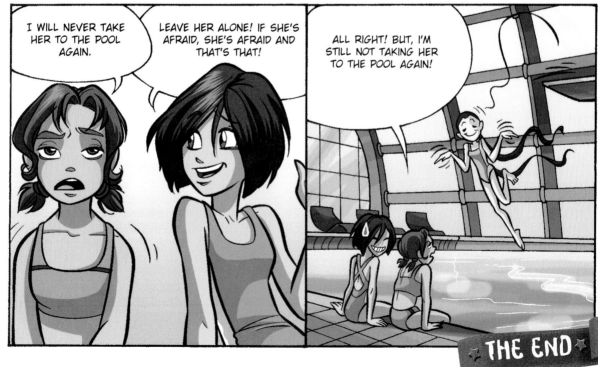

The Heart of Candracar

Guess your friend's birthday with the magic of the Heart of Candracar.

1 Ask a friend to point out all the pendants that contain her day of birth.

2 Highlight the number written above each pendant pointed out by your friend.

3 Now, ask her which pendants contain the number of her month of birth and highlight the number written underneath each pendant she pointed out.

4 Add up all the numbers highlighted at the top of the pendants.

16
16 17 18
19 20 21 22
23 24 25 26
27 28 29
30 31
16

8
8 9 10
11 12 13 14
15 24 25 26
27 28 29
30 31
8

1
1 3 5
7 9 11 13
15 17 19 21
23 25 27
29 31
1

4
4 5 6
7 12 13 14
15 20 21 22
23 28 29
30 31
4

2
2 3 6
7 10 11 14
15 18 19 22
23 26 27
30 31
2

5 Add up all the numbers highlighted at the bottom of the pendants.

6 The sum of the numbers ABOVE the pendants reveal the day and the sum of the numbers UNDERNEATH reveal your friend's month of birth. Magic!

I don't believe it! Will - dealing with numbers!
Taranee

55

HI, I'M HAY LIN

- ☻ My star sign is Gemini
- ☻ My birthday is June 4th
- ☻ I collect comic books and love science fiction
- ☻ My favourite colour is silver
- ☻ I'm very creative and love drawing and making my own clothes
- ☻ I'm enthusiastic, generous and optimistic – definitely the most positive of the group

AS A W.I.T.C.H.

- ☻ I control the power of air
- ☻ I'm the only one of the group who can fly

MY POWER IS AIR

Flights of imagination

LOOK, A CLOUD SHAPED LIKE A STARFISH!

WHERE?

RIGHT THERE, NEXT TO THE ONE THAT LOOKS LIKE A MAD HORSE!

SORRY, WHERE?

I ONLY SEE COTTONY CLOUDS. WHAT ABOUT YOU?

ME, TOO!

COME ON! TRY USING YOUR IMAGINATION.

MY IMAGINATION DOESN'T WORK THAT WAY!

MINE DOES. I CAN IMAGINE ANYTHING IF I TRY!

GET CREATIVE

Why not show the world who you really are by doing something creative? If you need inspiration, take a look around – anything and everything can trigger your imagination to give you loads of great ideas.

Imagination can make your dreams come true – just think creatively about how to reach your goal and you'll be one step closer to it. Let your creativity take control!

You can do it!

1 Imagination works like a muscle – the more you train it, the stronger it becomes.

2 Start by reading a book. Think of the exercise your brain is doing, imagining the images to go with the words!

3 Creativity uses the instinctive right side of the brain. So, relax and try one of the ideas on this page – you'll be surprised at what you can do!

Try a new sport

Jump with joy

Learn a new trick with playing cards

Paint

Write a poem or song

Sing

Make a photographic book of your most beautiful memories

The key to creativity is IMAGINATION

W.I.T.C.H. symbols

10 pts

Can you work out where each of the 7 symbols below fit into the grid? There must only ever be one of each symbol in each vertical and horizontal line.

Spot the differences

These two pictures of the W.I.T.C.H. girls may look the same but can you find all 7 differences in the bottom picture?

5 pts

Perfect portraits

We're all different in our own special way. Look carefully at these sketches of the W.I.T.C.H. girls, and then try copying them. How about sketching your own self portrait?

Cornelia
Her long, narrow face and elegant neck are the most important things to show.

Hay Lin
Look at Hay Lin's heart-shaped face. All the other elements can be added to this shape.

Irma
A round face and huge eyes are the features that stand out most for Irma.

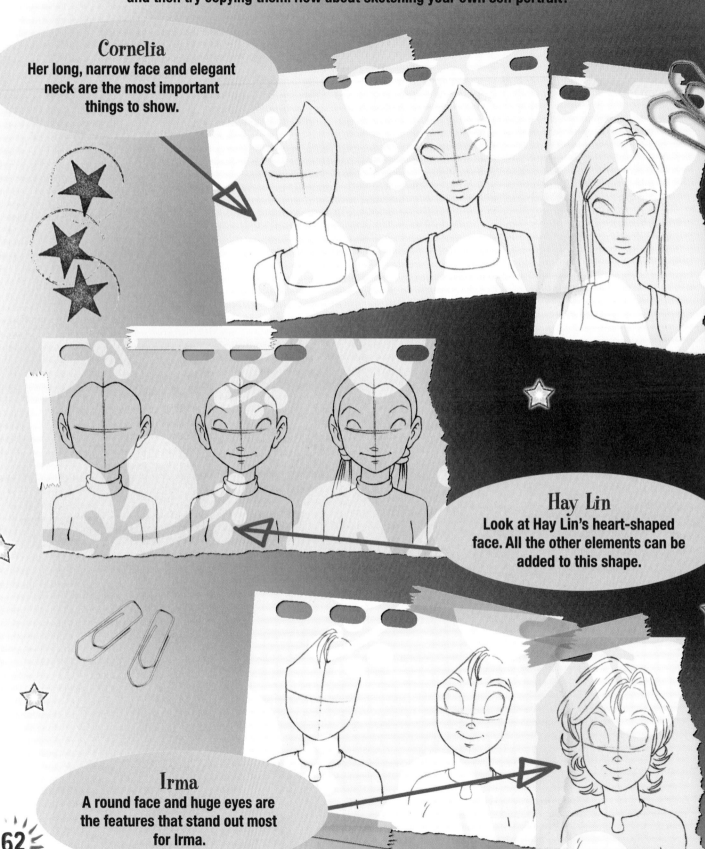

Taranee
With Taranee's short hair, it's important to get the position of her ears correct.

Hey, Taranee — your plait looks cool!

Irma

Will
Her delicate features are set-off well by her big mop of scruffy hair.

63

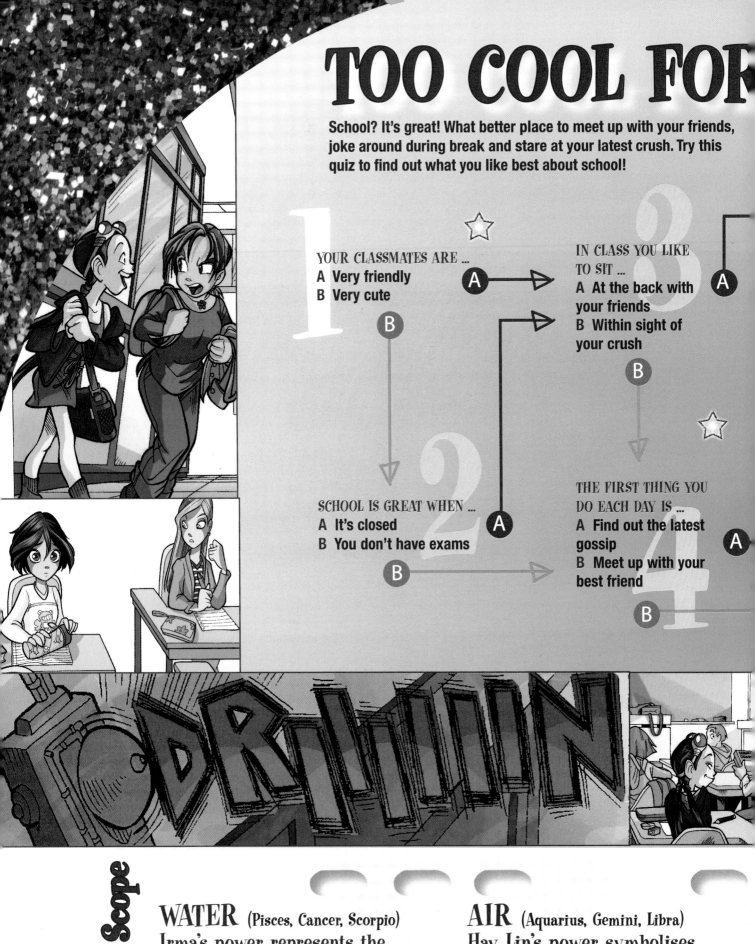

TOO COOL FOR

School? It's great! What better place to meet up with your friends, joke around during break and stare at your latest crush. Try this quiz to find out what you like best about school!

1

YOUR CLASSMATES ARE ...
A Very friendly
B Very cute

2

SCHOOL IS GREAT WHEN ...
A It's closed
B You don't have exams

3

IN CLASS YOU LIKE TO SIT ...
A At the back with your friends
B Within sight of your crush

4

THE FIRST THING YOU DO EACH DAY IS ...
A Find out the latest gossip
B Meet up with your best friend

WATER (Pisces, Cancer, Scorpio)
Irma's power represents the purity of all things.
Someone you admire will notice your talents. A new girl at school is set to become a firm friend.

AIR (Aquarius, Gemini, Libra)
Hay Lin's power symbolises freedom.
A music lesson will inspire you to be creative. Plus you'll find a new friendship in an unexpected place.

SCHOOL?

5

A GOOD LESSON MEANS YOU'VE ...

A Helped a friend with a problem
B Had a real laugh

A — Go to Profile 1

B

6

AT THE END OF SCHOOL YOU ...

A Hang out with your friends for as long as possible
B Count the hours until you see your crush again

A — Go to Profile 2

B — Go to Profile 3

Profile 1 – YOUR CLASSMATES

You really love chatting and telling your friends everything that happens to you. You can also understand straight away if someone is upset.

W.I.T.C.H. advice: Be careful not to ask too many personal questions. Somebody might take it the wrong way and think you're being nosey.

Profile 2 – THE BREAK

For you, breaks are magical. They give you a chance to hear all the latest gossip and jokes about your mates and teachers.

W.I.T.C.H. advice: If you see someone from your class alone at break, invite her to join your gang. The more the merrier, right?

Profile 3 – SEEING YOUR CRUSH

You can always think of the right thing to say ... except when your crush is within a mile from you!

W.I.T.C.H. advice: Use your holiday to "rehearse" possible conversations with him. When you're back at school you'll be ready to do some magic!

FIRE (Aries, Leo, Sagittarius)
Taranee's power is the emblem of generosity.
A teacher will fill you with inspiration. A lesson you normally find boring will become a real laugh.

EARTH (Taurus, Virgo, Capricorn)
Cornelia's power is solid and strong.
Take a chance and sign up for a new activity at school. You'll be great!

Puzzle answers

How did you get on - did you manage to finish all the puzzles?

Check your answers and add up your score.

Then turn the page to find out your W.I.T.C.H. level ...

Page 17
The alarm clock!

20 pts

Who's meeting who?

HI WILL!

WANT TO GO ON

A BIKE RIDE

AFTER SCHOOL?

5 pts

Page 19
Power match

10 pts

Quick search

5 pts

Page 27
Shell search

5 pts

Word wonder

10 words are – field, institute, held, stint, tent, shield, send, dense, less, test. You may have found others!

10 pts

Page 30
Smile!

Photo C

5 pts

Letter jumble

WATER

5 pts

Page 45

W.I.T.C.H. search

20 pts

```
M A G E R I E F W O S U F
G T I G C G R I A G T O I G
D R F P O W D F T S E T D R
E M P I H S B N C I A F C E
N S A S K C U L R S C L P U
E H E G H T A R E A B O I O
R I U D I F I E N E S D H P
G P M L U C K Y C H A R M D
Y B L A I W A T B A M R T H
```

The mysterious picture

1 = Will
2 = Taranee
3 = Irma
4 = Cornelia
5 = Hay Lin

5 pts

Page 50

Magic numbers

1	12	7	14
8	13	2	11
10	3	16	5
15	6	9	4

15 pts

Colour trail

10 pts

Page 61

W.I.T.C.H. symbols

10 pts

Spot the differences

5 pts

WHAT'S YOUR W.I.T.C.H. LEVEL?

0-30 pts

Er ... maybe you were a bit distracted and got lost in your dreams.
Why not have another go?
W.I.T.C.H. advice: Try again with a friend – then you can help each other!
W.I.T.C.H. level: WANNABE W.I.T.C.H.

31-55 pts

Well done! You just need the confidence to
believe you can do it to get a better score.
W.I.T.C.H. advice: Don't be afraid to give 100%!
W.I.T.C.H. level: APPRENTICE W.I.T.C.H.

56-85 pts

Good going, girl!
You are focused and good at reasoning.
Learn to love the rational side of you, too,
and you'll get an even higher score!
W.I.T.C.H. advice: Numbers have magic secrets, too!
W.I.T.C.H. level: ALMOST W.I.T.C.H.

86-110 pts

Wow! You're an interesting girl, capable of solving everything
with your imagination and quick thinking. Congratulations!
W.I.T.C.H. advice: Listen to your heart in order to always find the right way!
W.I.T.C.H. level: JUST W.I.T.C.H.

111-130 pts

Hey! You are B.A.E. (Beyond All Expectations!) When you
face a problem you give 100% and trust your instincts. Excellent!
W.I.T.C.H. advice: A piece of advice given
by a trusted friend can make things even better!
W.I.T.C.H. level: SUPER W.I.T.C.H.

Reach for the stars!

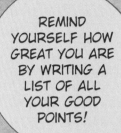

REMIND YOURSELF HOW GREAT YOU ARE BY WRITING A LIST OF ALL YOUR GOOD POINTS!

TELL YOUR DREAMS TO YOUR MATES SO YOU CAN WORK TOGETHER TO MAKE THEM HAPPEN!

TAKE THINGS SLOWLY AND YOU'LL GET THERE IN THE END!

HAVE A LAUGH WITH YOUR MATES. IT WILL MAKE YOU FEEL MORE POSITIVE!

REMEMBER, YOU CAN DO ANYTHING YOU SET YOUR MIND TO!

69